G000242236

ISLE OF MAN

foundations of a landscape

Written and illustrated by Elizabeth Pickett
Designed by Joyce Barclay

Published by the British Geological Survey
© NERC & Treasury, Isle of Man 2001

CONTENTS

The story of the Isle of Man and its landscape began in the distant geological past, hundreds of millions of years ago, long before the Island existed in its present form. Over millions of years the landmass containing the Isle of Man drifted through many of the Earth's latitudes and climates. The rocks that form the coasts, hills and plains of the Isle of Man tell of this journey - a fascinating story of a deep ocean and colliding continents, eroding mountains and arid plains, tropical seas and underwater volcanoes. Long extinct sea creatures are now preserved as fossils and provide a window to life millions of years ago.

In more recent geological times mighty ice sheets advanced over the Isle of Man. The immense power of the ice and its meltwaters ground down the rocks and shaped the bare bones of the landscape we see today. Following melting of the ice, rising sea levels began to sever the land links which connected the Isle of Man to Ireland and Britain. Finally, about 10 000 years ago, the Isle of Man became an island. Since then, the pounding seas and the rivers of its hills and glens have contributed to a constantly changing landscape. The first people arrived about 8000 years ago, heralding a new chapter in the evolution of the Island's landscape.

Geological processes have shaped the Isle of Man and the results have influenced the lives of the Manx people through the ages. The Island's rocks have particular characteristics because of the processes that formed them, and they produce distinctive building stones. The high hill tops and rugged coasts provided places of refuge in the Island's turbulent past, and minerals which formed deep underground have been mined to produce valuable metals.

The Isle of Man's landscape continues to change, its evolution driven by a combination of natural processes and human activity. This book describes the geological processes that have formed the Island's unique rocks and beautiful landscape, and how Manx people have used the rocks and natural features around them.

GEOLOGICAL TIME

Millions of years ago

Events affecting the Isle of Man

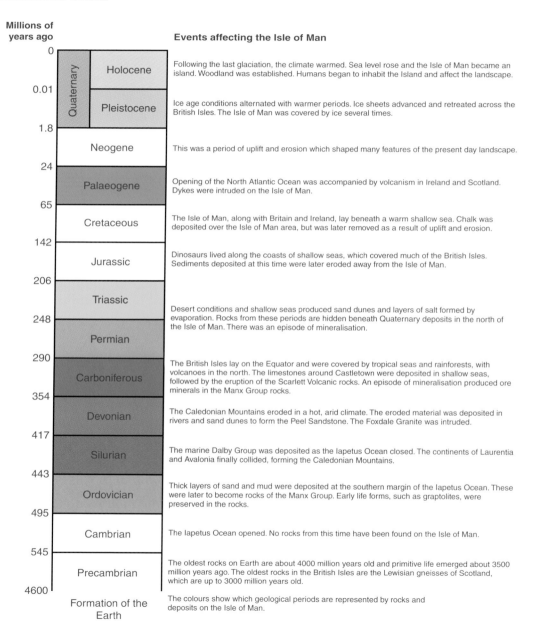

Millions of years ago	Period		Events affecting the Isle of Man
0	Quaternary	Holocene	Following the last glaciation, the climate warmed. Sea level rose and the Isle of Man became an island. Woodland was established. Humans began to inhabit the Island and affect the landscape.
0.01	Quaternary	Pleistocene	Ice age conditions alternated with warmer periods. Ice sheets advanced and retreated across the British Isles. The Isle of Man was covered by ice several times.
1.8		Neogene	This was a period of uplift and erosion which shaped many features of the present day landscape.
24		Palaeogene	Opening of the North Atlantic Ocean was accompanied by volcanism in Ireland and Scotland. Dykes were intruded on the Isle of Man.
65		Cretaceous	The Isle of Man, along with Britain and Ireland, lay beneath a warm shallow sea. Chalk was deposited over the Isle of Man area, but was later removed as a result of uplift and erosion.
142		Jurassic	Dinosaurs lived along the coasts of shallow seas, which covered much of the British Isles. Sediments deposited at this time were later eroded away from the Isle of Man.
206		Triassic	Desert conditions and shallow seas produced sand dunes and layers of salt formed by evaporation. Rocks from these periods are hidden beneath Quaternary deposits in the north of the Isle of Man. There was an episode of mineralisation.
248		Permian	
290		Carboniferous	The British Isles lay on the Equator and were covered by tropical seas and rainforests, with volcanoes in the north. The limestones around Castletown were deposited in shallow seas, followed by the eruption of the Scarlett Volcanic rocks. An episode of mineralisation produced ore minerals in the Manx Group rocks.
354		Devonian	The Caledonian Mountains eroded in a hot, arid climate. The eroded material was deposited in rivers and sand dunes to form the Peel Sandstone. The Foxdale Granite was intruded.
417		Silurian	The marine Dalby Group was deposited as the Iapetus Ocean closed. The continents of Laurentia and Avalonia finally collided, forming the Caledonian Mountains.
443		Ordovician	Thick layers of sand and mud were deposited at the southern margin of the Iapetus Ocean. These were later to become rocks of the Manx Group. Early life forms, such as graptolites, were preserved in the rocks.
495		Cambrian	The Iapetus Ocean opened. No rocks from this time have been found on the Isle of Man.
545		Precambrian	The oldest rocks on Earth are about 4000 million years old and primitive life emerged about 3500 million years ago. The oldest rocks in the British Isles are the Lewisian gneisses of Scotland, which are up to 3000 million years old.
4600			

Formation of the Earth

The colours show which geological periods are represented by rocks and deposits on the Isle of Man.

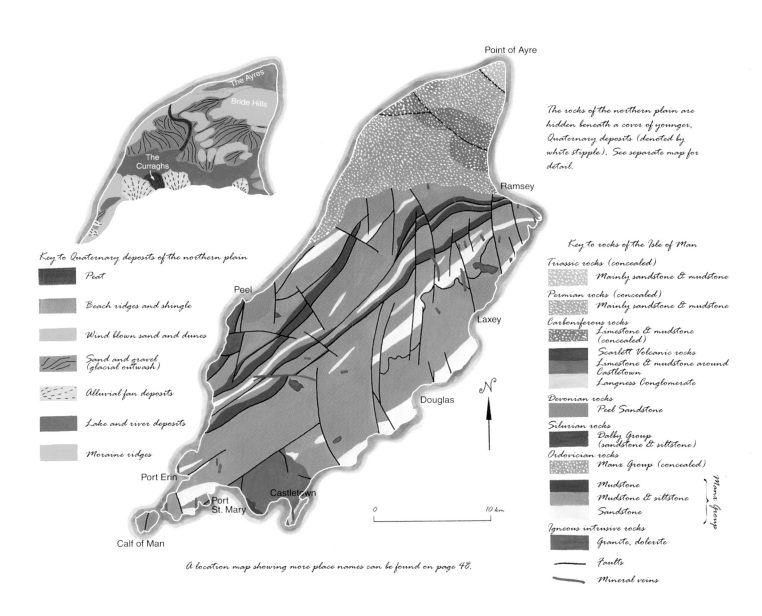

Point of Ayre

The rocks of the northern plain are hidden beneath a cover of younger, Quaternary deposits (denoted by white stipple). See separate map for detail.

The Ayres

Bride Hills

The Curraghs

Ramsey

Key to Quaternary deposits of the northern plain

Peat

Beach ridges and shingle

Wind blown sand and dunes

Sand and gravel (glacial outwash)

Alluvial fan deposits

Lake and river deposits

Moraine ridges

Peel

Laxey

Douglas

Port Erin

Castletown

Port St. Mary

Calf of Man

N

0   10 km

Key to rocks of the Isle of Man

Triassic rocks (concealed)
Mainly sandstone & mudstone

Permian rocks (concealed)
Mainly sandstone & mudstone

Carboniferous rocks
Limestone & mudstone (concealed)
Scarlett Volcanic rocks
Limestone & mudstone around Castletown
Langness Conglomerate

Devonian rocks
Peel Sandstone

Silurian rocks
Dalby Group (sandstone & siltstone)

Ordovician rocks
Manx Group (concealed)

Mudstone
Mudstone & siltstone   Manx Group
Sandstone

Igneous intrusive rocks
Granite, dolerite

Faults

Mineral veins

A location map showing more place names can be found on page 48.

Colliding continents and a vanished ocean

*T*hroughout the Earth's history continents have drifted over the surface of the planet, riding on huge plates which move apart and collide, causing oceans to open and close and mountain ranges to rise up and then erode away. This continuous process of change is called plate tectonics. Where plates move apart, molten rock (magma) rises and solidifies to create new ocean floor at mid-ocean ridges. This is happening today at the Mid Atlantic Ridge, where new rock is being formed and the continents of South America and Africa are moving apart at the rate of a few centimetres a year. Where plates collide, one descends beneath the other in a process called subduction. The descending plates cause earthquakes and chains of volcanoes such as those around the western rim of the Pacific Ocean. When continental masses collide, their edges buckle and crumple, forming mountain ranges. These are then gradually destroyed by the process of erosion.

How the world may have looked 500 million years ago. (A) represents the position of Scotland and (B) that of England, Wales and the Isle of Man.

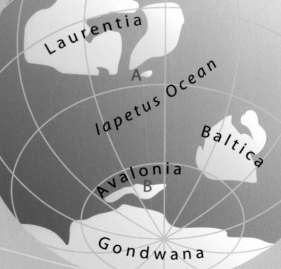

Laurentia

A

Iapetus Ocean

Baltica

Avalonia

B

Gondwana

The basic structure of the British Isles was shaped by plate tectonics. Over 500 million years ago, what is now northern and southern Britain was once separated by the Iapetus Ocean. Scotland and the northern part of Ireland were part of the continent of Laurentia, which also included North America and Greenland. England, Wales and the Isle of Man lay to the south of the Iapetus Ocean, on a small continental fragment known as Avalonia. To the south, the supercontinent of Gondwana included Africa, South America, India, Australia and Antarctica.

About 450 million years ago the Iapetus Ocean was a few thousand kilometres wide

NW

Laurentia

Iapetus Ocean
mid ocean ridge

Avalonia

SE

subduction zone

Scotland and
Northern Ireland

Caledonian Mountains

England, Wales,
Isle of Man and
southern Ireland

NW

SE

The Iapetus Ocean closed about 410 million years ago

About 470 million years ago the floor of the Iapetus Ocean started to subduct and the ocean began to close. Volcanoes developed along the margins of the ocean in what was to become Scotland, Wales and the Lake District. About 410 million years ago Avalonia collided with the continent of Laurentia, forming the Caledonian Mountains and bringing together the northern and southern parts of the British Isles. The seam along which they joined runs through the Solway Firth and skirts the northwestern edge of the Isle of Man.

Rocks from the Iapetus Ocean

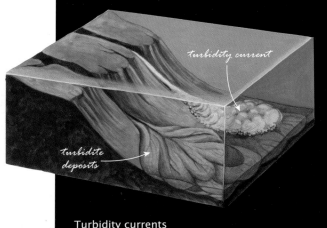

Turbidity currents depositing sediments at the margins of an ocean.

*T*he hilly backbone of the Isle of Man and many of its rugged coasts are composed of a thick sequence of rocks known collectively as the Manx Group (previously called the Manx Slates). These were deposited as layers of sand, silt and mud at the southern margin of the Iapetus Ocean about 490 to 470 million years ago, during the Ordovician Period. Many of these layers of sediment were produced by turbidity currents, sediment-laden water currents caused by underwater avalanches of loose material at the margins of continents.

In the quiet periods between these avalanche events, fine muds and the remains of small creatures settled on the ocean floor. These layers are preserved today as mudstone containing fossils such as graptolites and acritarchs. Graptolites were planktonic colonies in which hundreds or thousands of tiny polyp-like animals lived in a series of small cups arranged along slender skeletal structures. Acritarchs are microscopic, hollow structures made of organic material and are of uncertain origin. These two fossil groups are important in the dating and correlating of Ordovician and Silurian rocks.

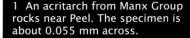

1 An acritarch from Manx Group rocks near Peel. The specimen is about 0.055 mm across.

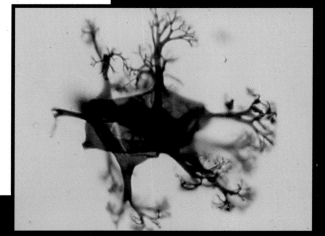

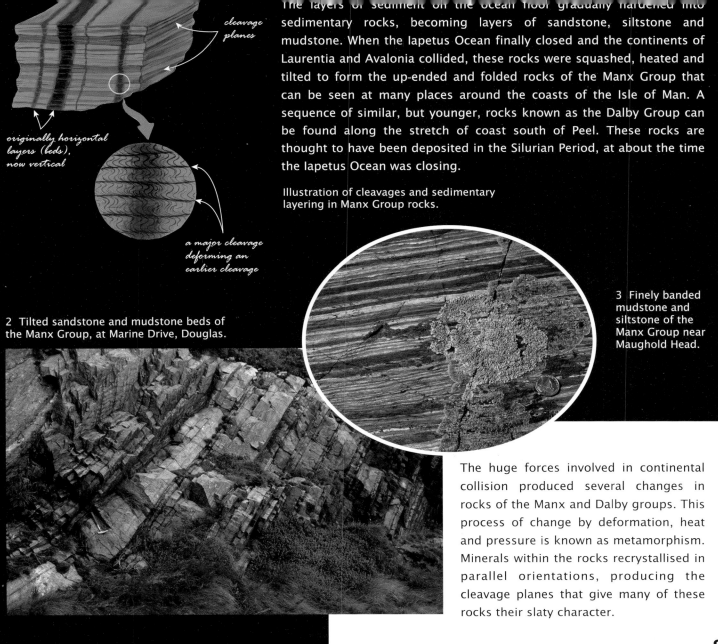

cleavage planes

originally horizontal layers (beds), now vertical

a major cleavage deforming an earlier cleavage

The layers of sediment on the ocean floor gradually hardened into sedimentary rocks, becoming layers of sandstone, siltstone and mudstone. When the Iapetus Ocean finally closed and the continents of Laurentia and Avalonia collided, these rocks were squashed, heated and tilted to form the up-ended and folded rocks of the Manx Group that can be seen at many places around the coasts of the Isle of Man. A sequence of similar, but younger, rocks known as the Dalby Group can be found along the stretch of coast south of Peel. These rocks are thought to have been deposited in the Silurian Period, at about the time the Iapetus Ocean was closing.

Illustration of cleavages and sedimentary layering in Manx Group rocks.

2 Tilted sandstone and mudstone beds of the Manx Group, at Marine Drive, Douglas.

3 Finely banded mudstone and siltstone of the Manx Group near Maughold Head.

The huge forces involved in continental collision produced several changes in rocks of the Manx and Dalby groups. This process of change by deformation, heat and pressure is known as metamorphism. Minerals within the rocks recrystallised in parallel orientations, producing the cleavage planes that give many of these rocks their slaty character.

9

Cairns and crosses

*E*ver since people first came to the Isle of Man, some 8000 years ago, their lives have been inextricably linked with the geology and landscape of the Island. In particular, the Manx Group rocks, which give the Island its hilly spine and much of its spectacular rocky coastline, have affected the way people live and work, their culture and their beliefs.

4 A defensive site on high ground - the Bronze Age hillfort on the summit of South Barrule.

5 The Neolithic chambered tomb of Cashtal yn Ard, near Maughold.

The sheer, rocky coastlines of Manx and Dalby Group rocks provided excellent defensive sites. On the slate headlands of the south are the remains of many Iron Age promontory forts which date back almost 2000 years. The fort at Cronk ny Merriu (6 below) is protected on three sides by sea cliffs and, on its vulnerable landward side, by a bank and ditch. Nearly a thousand years later the fort was reoccupied by Vikings. The remains of a Norse longhouse can be seen next to the much older bank and ditch.

About 5000 years ago, in Neolithic times, people buried their dead in monumental chambered tombs whose great stone slabs were hewn from local Manx Group rocks. The cairns of rubble which once covered the tombs have long since been stripped away, leaving the stone slabs as a dramatic legacy from the Island's past.

7 Thorwald's Cross, Kirk Andreas.

With the introduction of Christianity into the Isle of Man 1500 years ago there began a period of great artistic achievement which lasted some 400 years. The outstanding Celtic and Norse carved crosses for which the Isle of Man is famous date from this time. The crosses were carved from local Manx Group rocks and range from crude markings on boulders to elaborate and beautiful works of art with inscriptions and dedications. The earliest crosses date from AD 650 to 800 and show Celtic styles with commemorations in Ogham (ancient Celtic lettering) or Latin. Examples of these Celtic crosses can be seen at Kirk Maughold, Old Kirk Lonan and the Manx Museum.

9 Dragon Cross, Kirk Michael.

8 Gaut's Cross, Kirk Michael.

When the Vikings began to settle on the Isle of Man from AD 800 and converted to Christianity, they continued the cross carving tradition, decorating their crosses with scenes from Norse mythology and runic inscriptions. Outstanding examples of Norse crosses were carved by Gaut, the best known of the Scandinavian sculptors. On one cross he proudly wrote 'Gaut made this and all in Mann'. Norse crosses can be seen at the parish churches of Andreas, Maughold, Jurby, Michael, Old Kirk Braddan and Ballaugh Old Church.

Castles and crofts

*I*f you travel around the Isle of Man you will see rocks of the Manx and Dalby groups in many walls and buildings. These rocks contain bedding planes (formed when they were originally deposited in layers), and a range of cleavage planes (formed during episodes of deformation). These planes cause the rocks to split in various ways, producing blocks, slabs and slices. A typical wall is made of slabs laid horizontally, with a course of slanting stones laid on edge on top of the wall. Many of these walls were built by Scottish 'dry stane dykers' in the 18th and 19th centuries. Rocks from the Manx and Dalby groups are also found in many of the Island's buildings. The 15th century castle wall enclosing St. Patrick's Isle is made of Dalby Group slate slabs, some of which were laid on edge to give the walls the appearance of being more substantial than they really are. Dark slate from the Manx Group in Sulby Glen was used to build St. Stephen's Church, Sulby, and Kirk Bride Church.

10 TOP: Upland wall of Manx Group rocks.

11 ABOVE: 15th century curtain walls at Peel Castle, composed of Dalby Group slate blocks laid on edge.

12 RIGHT: The Sugar Loaf, near Spanish Head. Lintel stones were quarried from cliffs in this area.

Quarries in the Manx Group at Spanish Head and near Ballaugh were used for producing lintels during the 18th and 19th centuries. Lintels from these quarries were used over doors and windows and for gate posts and bridges. Single pieces of rock over 5 metres in length were obtained from Spanish Head in the 19th century and used for flooring in Castle Rushen at Castletown.

14 Cregneash village in 1992.

The crofters' cottages which were common all over the Island until about 100 years ago, were mostly made of Manx Group rocks. Their traditional thatched roofs, some of which can still be seen at Cregneash, were gradually replaced by slate from local quarries. Very few buildings have Manx slate roofs today but some local slates can still be seen on the Old Grammar School at Castletown.

13 Building stone from the Manx Group.

15 The 19th century boarding houses of Douglas Promenade are built from Manx Group rocks that were quarried at Douglas Head and Summer Hill. The stone was then covered with a layer of render and stucco.

During the 18th and 19th centuries much effort was put into searching for sources of good roofing slate on the Island. Many slate trials and quarries were opened up, particularly during the mid 19th century. Although Manx newspapers of the day reported many promising finds of slate, it proved to be of generally unreliable quality. Good roofing slate such as Welsh slate can be split along cleavage planes to produce thin, even slices of rock. The complexity in the structure of slate from the Manx and Dalby groups means that the rocks tend to split into irregular and often thick pieces. Towards the end of the 19th century the availability of good slate from Wales caused the slate industry on the Island to decline. Many deserted quarries with their spoil heaps and ruins, such as those at South Barrule, Glen Rushen and Sartfell, can still be seen in the hills. However, the industry did not die out completely and slate is still worked today from a few quarries, including one at South Barrule.

Igneous intrusive rocks from deep within the Earth

When molten rock (magma) rises through the Earth's crust and cools before it reaches the surface it solidifies to form great masses called igneous intrusions. After millions of years of erosion these rocks may be exposed at the Earth's surface. By looking at these rocks we can see the innards of ancient magma chambers which cooled slowly deep within the Earth to produce a range of hard, crystalline rocks of different compositions. Rocks such as granite, dolerite and diorite are formed in this way. The Isle of Man has a variety of igneous intrusions which range from irregular dome-like masses of granite to sheet-like intrusions (known as dykes) of dolerite and diorite.

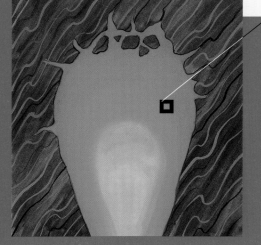

An intrusion of molten rock into the Earth's crust.

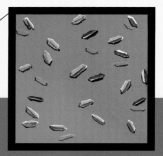

Crystals forming in magma as it cools.

The oldest igneous intrusion on the Isle of Man is probably the Poortown Dolerite near Peel. Dolerite is a hard, crystalline rock that contains the minerals plagioclase (a type of feldspar) and pyroxene, and locally olivine. It is a finer grained version of the rock known as gabbro and the intrusion has traditionally been called the Poortown Gabbro. It is thought that the Poortown Dolerite was intruded into Manx Group rocks over 450 million years ago, during the Ordovician Period. It may have been related to volcanic eruptions which occurred during subduction of the Iapetus Ocean.

16 A microscopic view of the Foxdale Granite. The image is 3.5 mm wide.

The best known and largest of the Manx intrusions are the granites at Foxdale and Dhoon. A smaller intrusion containing both granite and gabbro also occurs at Oatlands in the southeast of the Island but is not well exposed, and is best seen as rocks in the surrounding field walls. All these outcrops are the tips of much larger intrusions hidden at depth. They were intruded during closure of the Iapetus Ocean and eventual continental collision. The Dhoon Granite was intruded before the Foxdale Granite, which dates from about 400 million years ago. The heat given off by these intrusions before they cooled caused the surrounding rocks to become baked and altered so that slate close to the granites has a silvery appearance. The pale grey Foxdale Granite is made of interlocking crystals of quartz, feldspar and muscovite (a silvery white variety of mica). On Stoney Mountain the granite contains veins of white quartz and mica, known locally as 'spar' veins. The Dhoon Granite, by contrast, is finer grained than the Foxdale Granite and contains a dark variety of mica known as biotite. In the quarry at Dhoon the rock contains quartz veins which include the mineral tourmaline.

17 A microscopic view of the Poortown Dolerite. The image is 3.5 mm wide.

18 A dolerite dyke that has intruded limestone at Scarlett. The dyke is about 55 million years old and the limestone is 350-300 million years old.

Dykes can be seen in many places around the Isle of Man. These were intruded at various times during the geological history of the Island and have a range of compositions. They include igneous rocks known as dolerite, diorite and lamprophyre. The dolerite dykes are dark and fine grained and some are part of a huge swarm of dykes that extends across Northern Ireland and Scotland. These formed during the creation of the Atlantic Ocean and are about 55 million years old.

IGNEOUS ROCKS
Axes and aggregate

Igneous rocks on the Isle of Man have been quarried through the centuries for a variety of purposes. They are hard, dense and durable, and can be broken along fractures into regular blocks. These qualities have made them valuable rocks for a range of tools and implements, as well as for building and road stone. The earliest known use of igneous rocks on the Island was around 3000 BC, in Neolithic times. Several stone axe heads excavated at Ronaldsway were found to be made of diorite from a nearby dyke. Diorite is a speckled, greenish rock made of white plagioclase (a type of feldspar) and dark green hornblende. However, many other stone axes found on the Isle of Man probably came from Neolithic 'axe factories' in Britain and Northern Ireland, such as those in Cumbria and County Antrim.

19 Neolithic axes made of diorite.

20 Granite cannon balls from Peel Castle.

Cannon balls made of Manx granite have been found at Peel Castle, testifying to the Island's turbulent past. A more domestic use has been the production of hand mills or querns, some of which date back hundreds of years. Granite from quarries at Foxdale, Dhoon and Oatlands can be seen in the Island's buildings and walls. Granite is recognisable by its coarse grained crystals, grey colour and sparkling mica. One of the Island's best known buildings, St. John's Church, by Tynwald Hill, was built of Foxdale Granite from Stoney Mountain. Granite was used for many cottages and barns in the Foxdale area and for strengthening the corners of houses built from other kinds of stone.

Granite was also used to make large millstones for watermills, water troughs and agricultural stone rollers. In the 19th century Manx granite was exported to the industrial towns of northern England for use as paving stones and kerbs. Records from the Foxdale quarry at the beginning of the 20th century show that the granite was mainly being used for engineering purposes, stone rollers, paving setts, kerbs, millstones and road chippings. The quartz-mica 'spar' veins which occur in the Foxdale Granite have been worked for use in dashing buildings and ornamenting walls. In recent times Foxdale Granite was used to extend the Battery Pier at Douglas and is still quarried today at Stoney Mountain to provide crushed rock aggregate, building stone and armour stone for coastal protection work.

Granite boulders, which were plucked and carried away from their bedrock sources by ice sheets during the last glaciation, have also been used in the past. Scattered boulders of Foxdale Granite were removed from fields and used in walls and buildings.

The Poortown Dolerite is extracted and crushed at Poortown quarry, southeast of Peel. The quarry was opened around 1870 and is still worked today as the Isle of Man's main source of aggregate for road building.

23 Poortown quarry, where dolerite is extracted for road stone.

21 BACKGROUND: St. John's Church.
22 BELOW: St. John's Church and Tynwald Hill.

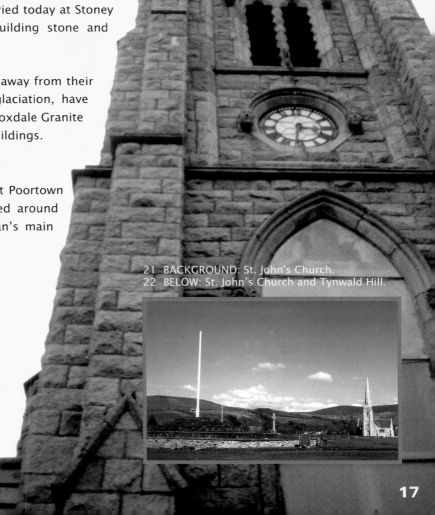

Flash floods and desert dunes

The Caledonian mountains, which formed by continental collision about 410 million years ago, were of Alpine proportions. Over millions of years they were eroded and worn down by the action of wind and water. Great volumes of sand were carried to lower ground by streams and rivers, into a landscape of large river systems, flood plains, shallow lakes and sand dunes. This was the Devonian Period and the British Isles lay just south of the Equator. The climate was hot and semi-arid, with seasonal rainfall. Simple plants such as mosses had begun to colonise the land and the freshwater lakes contained primitive fish.

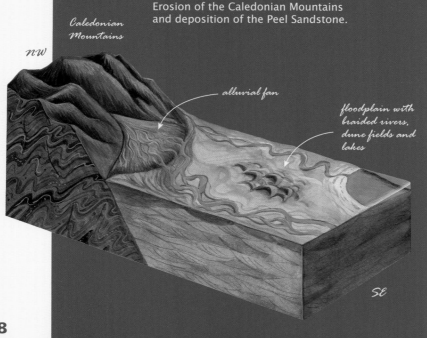

Erosion of the Caledonian Mountains and deposition of the Peel Sandstone.

Caledonian Mountains

nw

alluvial fan

floodplain with braided rivers, dune fields and lakes

SE

On the Isle of Man this period of geological time is represented by the red rocks along the coast at Peel. Known collectively as the Peel Sandstone, these rocks are the relics of a vast system of braided rivers, alluvial fans, dune fields and lakes. They include sandstone, conglomerate and mudstone which were laid down as sand, pebbles and mud around 400 million years ago. Ripples and other indicators of water currents are preserved in many of the rocks and show that the rivers flowed southeastwards from mountains that lay to the northwest of the Isle of Man.

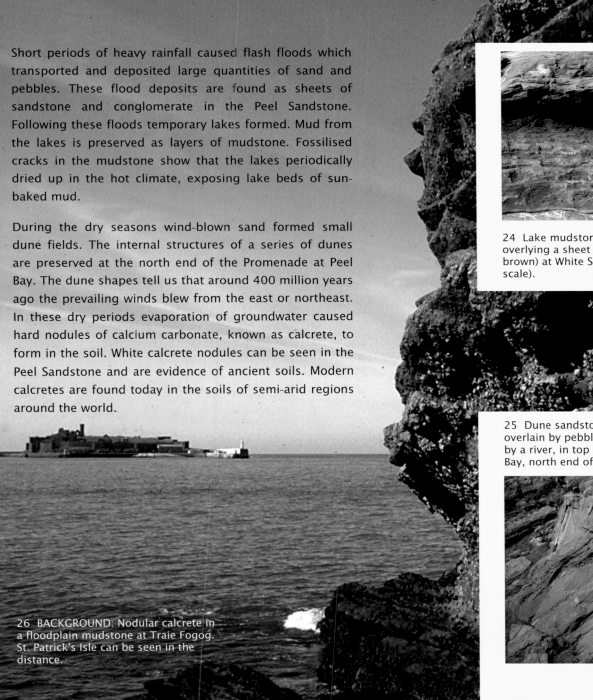

Short periods of heavy rainfall caused flash floods which transported and deposited large quantities of sand and pebbles. These flood deposits are found as sheets of sandstone and conglomerate in the Peel Sandstone. Following these floods temporary lakes formed. Mud from the lakes is preserved as layers of mudstone. Fossilised cracks in the mudstone show that the lakes periodically dried up in the hot climate, exposing lake beds of sun-baked mud.

During the dry seasons wind-blown sand formed small dune fields. The internal structures of a series of dunes are preserved at the north end of the Promenade at Peel Bay. The dune shapes tell us that around 400 million years ago the prevailing winds blew from the east or northeast. In these dry periods evaporation of groundwater caused hard nodules of calcium carbonate, known as calcrete, to form in the soil. White calcrete nodules can be seen in the Peel Sandstone and are evidence of ancient soils. Modern calcretes are found today in the soils of semi-arid regions around the world.

24 Lake mudstone (reddish brown) overlying a sheet flood sandstone (pale brown) at White Strand (lens cap for scale).

25 Dune sandstone to left of geologist, overlain by pebbly sandstone, deposited by a river, in top part of picture. Peel Bay, north end of Promenade.

26 BACKGROUND: Nodular calcrete in a floodplain mudstone at Traie Fogog. St. Patrick's Isle can be seen in the distance.

The Island's freestone

The Peel Sandstone is the Isle of Man's only 'freestone', a rock that can be cut and worked in any direction without fracturing. It was therefore valued as a building stone in the past and has been quarried for centuries at the Creg Malin quarry on a headland north of Peel Bay. This quarry supplied building stone for most of the old houses of Peel and probably for parts of Peel Castle. The warm red colour of the Peel Sandstone is caused by the presence of iron oxide and has made it a popular decorative stone.

27 Red Peel Sandstone within the walls of Peel Castle.

29 Peel Castle on St. Patrick's Isle, showing the Round Tower within the 15th century walls.

28 A microscopic view of the Peel Sandstone showing grains of quartz (white) cemented together by the dark reddish iron oxide that gives the Peel Sandstone its colour. Image is 5.5 mm wide.

Square blocks of Peel Sandstone were used to build the 12th century Round Tower which lies inside the walls of Peel Castle on St. Patrick's Isle. This impressive tower, whose doorway lies many feet off the ground, dates from the time of Viking raids on the Isle of Man and was probably built as a lookout and place of refuge for the monks of St. Patrick's Isle. Parts of the gatehouse and remaining walls of the 14th century Peel Castle are built of Peel Sandstone. Later, in the 15th century, imposing walls of grey slate were built to enclose the whole of the isle.

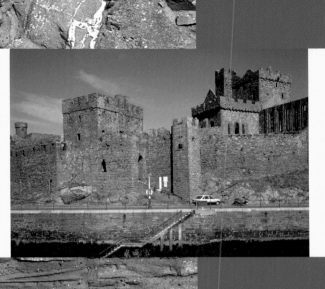

St. German's Cathedral was built on St. Patrick's Isle in the 13th century and many of its arches and windows are edged with decorative red Peel Sandstone. However, not all the sandstone you see around windows is Peel Sandstone. This fine grained sandstone is easily weathered away by the elements and in the past harder yellowish sandstone was imported from Cumbria.

30 The gatehouse and walls of Peel Castle enclosing St. German's Cathedral. Red Peel Sandstone forms most of the lower parts of the walls.

In more recent times, blocks of Peel Sandstone were used in the construction of the original breakwater at Peel in the 1860s. The old Wesleyan School can still be seen and was built of Peel Sandstone in 1861. In the 1870s, when the Manx steam railway was being constructed, Peel Sandstone was used for viaducts and stations between Peel and Ramsey. Between 1875 and 1884 the sandstone was quarried for the new Peel church and from 1900 to 1905 it was used to build the dam at Baldwin reservoir. However, the softness of the sandstone and the availability of other materials led to a decline in its use as a building stone and the red sandstone seen in many modern buildings around the Island today is not actually Peel Sandstone, but a more hard wearing sandstone imported from England.

31 Peel Sandstone used as a decorative stone around the arches of St. German's Cathedral.

Tropical seas flood the land

About 350 to 300 million years ago, during the Carboniferous Period, the British Isles lay on the Equator and the climate was hot and humid. Peaty swamps and dense rainforests of primitive trees covered large areas of Britain and marine life flourished in clear tropical seas. Fluctuating sea levels produced a constantly changing coastline and areas of rainforest were periodically submerged and drowned.

The story of this part of the Isle of Man's past began about 350 million years ago, with a conglomerate, a rock made of pebbles, cobbles and boulders. This is the Langness Conglomerate which forms stacks and arches on the west side of the Langness Peninsula. The conglomerate lies on nearly vertical slaty rocks of the Manx Group. The sharp contact between the two rock types is an example of an unconformity and represents a break of over 100 million years between formation of the slate and the conglomerate. During this time continental collision caused the slate to become deformed and tilted. Fragments were eroded off the slate and the action of water rounded them into pebbles which later became cemented together to form the Langness Conglomerate. The land was then inundated by tropical seas and the overlying fossil-rich limestone began to form.

32 Langness Conglomerate lying on top of slate of the Manx Group (pale grey). The sharp boundary is an unconformity.

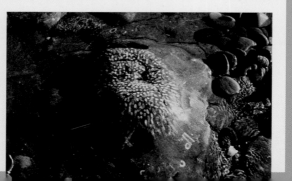

33 A fossil colonial coral on the shore at Poyllvaaish.

A Carboniferous tropical sea, rich in marine creatures which are now preserved as fossils in the Island's limestone.

The Carboniferous limestone in the south of the Isle of Man was mainly formed from the tiny calcium carbonate shells of plankton-sized marine animals called foraminifera. However, many other creatures inhabited these warm seas. Crinoids (also known as sea lilies) swayed in the currents, capturing food particles with their tentacles. Animals with shells, such as brachiopods, bivalves and gastropods, lived in the ooze on the sea floor. Fan-shaped bryozoan colonies and algal mats produced reef-like structures which supported several varieties of coral. Ammonoids, nautiloids and shark-like fish swam in the clear water. The fossils of corals, crinoids, brachiopods and gastropods can be found in the limestone on the shores at Derbyhaven, Castletown and Poyllvaaish.

34 Limestone (pale grey) alternating with mudstone (dark grey) at Scarlett Point. The surface in the foreground represents an ancient sea floor.

Layers (beds) of limestone, the top of each representing an ancient sea floor surface, can be seen around the south coast at Port St. Mary and Castletown. Many of these surfaces contain features such as fossilised ripples, mud mounds and fossil-rich hummocky structures. Layers of dark mudstone, which occur between some of the limestone beds, represent periods when dissolved oxygen was in short supply and the water did not support much life.

Stone for building and burning

35 Detail of limestone stonework at Castle Rushen.

*L*imestone from the Castletown area in the south of the Island is a hard wearing building stone which is easily worked, being layered and well jointed. Castle Rushen, one of the Isle of Man's most famous and historic buildings, is made of the pale grey limestone, as are many of the old buildings of Castletown. Historically, much of the building stone came from the shores around Scarlett, the Island's main source of limestone for many centuries. Limestone from a quarry at Scarlett supplied the rock for the Langness Lighthouse which was built in 1880 and crushed limestone from Scarlett was also used in the construction of the Douglas piers.

36 The imposing towers of Castle Rushen.

37 The water-filled old limestone quarry at Scarlett.

From the 14th to the 19th centuries a dark coloured limestone was quarried at Poyllvaaish, on the coast west of Castletown. Known as 'black marble' (although it is not a true marble), this limestone was used as a decorative rock. In the 14th century it was used at Rushen Abbey and for lintels in Castle Rushen. The rock was also popular for mantelpieces, flagstones, tombstones and steps. One layer of the limestone was particularly sought after. It contains fossil bivalve shells which the 19th century quarrymen called 'cockles'. Many mantelpieces in Douglas boarding houses were made of Poyllvaaish black marble. However, the rock did not polish well and was often coated with black varnish. It is not a hard wearing rock and many old tombstones of black marble have not weathered well. Although 19th century quarrying of the black marble ceased in the 1880s, the quarry is being worked again today. Recently, black marble has been used to make a series of commemorative Millennium 2000 crosses which can be seen around the Island.

In the 18th and 19th centuries, limestone was also extensively used in the production of lime for agricultural use. Ships carrying limestone would sail around the Island and dump their cargoes on beaches for farmers to collect and burn in their own lime kilns. As long ago as 1682 there are records of boats overloaded with limestone sinking near Douglas. Later, most of the lime-burning was carried out in large kilns at Derbyhaven, Scarlett, Ballasalla and Port St. Mary. Limestone is quarried today at Billown and Turkeyland. The limestone is crushed and used for producing lime and as aggregate for foundations and road bases.

39 Old lime kilns at Scarlett.

Eruptions from underwater volcanoes

*T*he Carboniferous Period was also a time of intense volcanic activity in parts of the British Isles. Volcanic ash and molten rock in the form of basalt lava flows were erupted from numerous volcanoes in the Midland Valley of Scotland. On the Isle of Man, lava and ash poured from volcanic vents that were probably mainly underwater on to a sea floor of limestone and mudstone. In contact with sea water the lava cooled rapidly and solidified into 'pillow lava'. Pillow lava is formed when a thin, glassy crust forms around a bulbous lump of newly erupted lava. Pressure builds up until the crust breaks and lava bursts through to form a new 'pillow'. As a pile of pillow lava builds up, the individual pillows sag around each other. Divers have observed pillow lavas forming in present-day underwater lava flows around Hawaii. Lava on the Isle of Man also cooled into columnar structures. These columns form the Stack at Scarlett and are similar to the spectacular hexagonal lava columns at the Giant's Causeway in County Antrim, Northern Ireland.

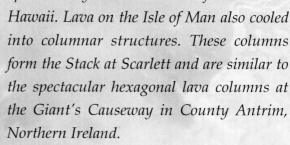

Pillow lava forming above an underwater volcanic vent.

40 BACKGROUND: Recent eruption of an Hawaiian volcano.

The basalt lavas from these ancient eruptions can be seen today between the Stack of Scarlett and Close ny Chollagh. They are fine grained and dark grey, brown or black in colour. Some of the rocks contain small cavities (vesicles) which were formed when bubbles of gas were trapped as the lava cooled. Much later, crystals of minerals such as calcite formed in the holes. When vesicles are filled with minerals they are known as amygdales. To the west of Scarlett the volcanic rocks include greenish coloured tuff. This would have been erupted explosively above the water surface as volcanic ash. It was then deposited on the volcano's flanks by underwater avalanches of ash and other volcanic debris.

41 Angular fragment of volcanic rock (about 10 cm across) showing vesicles formed by gas bubbles.

43 Lava (blocky rock in top half of small cliff) lying on beds of mudstone and limestone. The bedded rocks originally lay on the sea bed and were baked hard by the molten rock as it erupted.

42 Pillow lava near Close ny Chollagh Point.

Manx minerals and the earliest miners

Mineral deposits on the Isle of Man occur in steeply inclined veins which occupy faults and fissures in the Manx Group rocks and the granites. The ores of lead, zinc, copper and iron have all been mined commercially and small quantities of silver, present within the lead ore, have also been recovered. The main ore minerals are galena (lead sulphide), sphalerite (zinc iron sulphide), chalcopyrite (copper iron sulphide) and hematite (iron oxide). These ores are usually accompanied by uneconomic (gangue) minerals of which the most abundant are quartz, calcite, dolomite, siderite, baryte and pyrite. Antimony, molybdenum, nickel and uranium ore minerals also occur on the Isle of Man but have never been found in workable concentrations.

44 Manx minerals, including galena (grey, bottom left), hematite (black, centre right), white quartz and yellow dolomite (top right) and dolomite (yellow, bottom right).

The mineral veins were formed much later than the Manx Group rocks and the granites, perhaps during several episodes of mineralisation between about 320 and 220 million years ago. During these episodes hot fluids, rich in dissolved minerals from deep within the Earth, penetrated cracks and fissures in the rocks. Minerals from these fluids crystallised within the fissures. Most of the Island's mineral veins are orientated north-south, although some at Foxdale are east-west. Veins up to 11 metres wide have been reported from the Foxdale mines, although 1.5 metres or less is more typical.

Mineral-rich fluids, heated by hot rock at depth, rise and enter fractured rock.

The story of metal mining on the Isle of Man began several thousand years ago. Around 2000 BC, Bronze Age people on the Island knew how to smelt copper and tin to produce bronze, and may have used local copper ore from Bradda Head and Langness. Prehistoric stone hammers found at Bradda are thought to have been used for breaking the rock to get at the ore. A hoard of bronze objects and a lump of copper found at Ballagawne, Lonan, provide evidence of local bronzesmithing. Local lead may also have been used to improve the flow of the molten bronze.

45 View of Bradda Head across Port Erin Bay.

46 Cliff at Bradda Head showing the line of mineralisation behind old mine buildings.

47 Hematite of the 'kidney ore' variety from Maughold.

About 500 BC iron smelting technology arrived on the Isle of Man. People probably recognised red stains from hematite (iron ore) in the rocks at Maughold and may have started using local ore. The discovery of lumps of hematite with fragments of slag suggest that there was an iron smelting workshop at Kiondroghad near Kirk Andreas between the 7th and 9th centuries AD. A Norse runic inscription referring to 'Athakan the Smith' is the earliest written evidence of metal working on the Island.

From the Lords of Mann to the Lady Isabella

Harald, the Norse King of Mann and the Isles, provides the first written evidence of mining on the Isle of Man. In 1246 he issued a charter to the Abbot of Furness and his monks in which he refers to 'the use of all kinds of mines which may be found within my kingdom'. He also granted the monks some land at 'Rakenaldwath' as a 'repository for their minerals'. Since traces of a 14th or 15th century lead smelting workshop have been discovered at Ronaldsway, it seems likely that the charter related to this site. In 1292, after the demise of Norse power, a letter from King Edward I, then Lord of Mann, to his Governor of the Island spoke of digging for 'lead ore in our mine of Calf in the aforesaid Isle'. The lead was to be used for roofing a castle in Scotland and there is also documentary evidence of lead being exported to roof castles in Wales in the 1290s.

48 The washing floors at Laxey in the late 19th century. Here, the rock was crushed, sorted and washed to separate out the metal ores.

Mining for a range of metals continued through the centuries. Lead and iron mines were mentioned in Henry IV's 1406 grant of the Island to Sir John Stanley, and in 1667 Charles II allowed the Earl of Derby to mine for gold and silver. By the end of the 17th century, iron mines at Maughold were being worked and the Island was also producing significant amounts of copper and lead. However, it was between 1850 and 1890 that mining reached its heyday and the Manx mines became some of the most productive in the British Isles. They have contributed about 20% of all the zinc ever produced in the British Isles and around 5% of the lead.

49 ABOVE LEFT: The Foxdale mines in 1887.
50 ABOVE: Miners at Foxdale in the late 19th century.

Several ores were often worked from the same mine. Great Laxey, for example, produced lead and zinc. Copper and lead were mined at Bradda, and Foxdale yielded mainly lead. Small amounts of silver were also produced from these mines as a by-product of lead smelting. By the end of the 19th century, the Manx mining industry had begun to decline, mainly as a result of the discovery of higher grade ore in other parts of the world. Exhaustion of the easily accessible parts of the ore also meant that much more expense was required to make deeper shafts. In the last years of mining at Glen Rushen, near Foxdale, the ore was being worked at depths of over 600 metres below the surface. Intermittent mining continued into the early part of the 20th century with the last attempts at working the Great Laxey mine ceasing in the late 1930s.

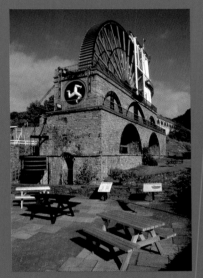

51 The Lady Isabella, now restored as a popular tourist site.

52 Townshend's Mine, from which lead was mined in the 1870s and 1880s.

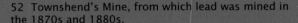

Today, evidence of the Isle of Man's mining past can be seen all over the Island. The ruins of mine buildings cling to the cliffs above the sea at Bradda Head and mine chimneys still dominate the landscape at Greeba, Glen Rushen and Foxdale. The greatest relic of all is the 'Lady Isabella', the great wheel at Laxey, which was built in 1854 to pump water out of the Laxey mine.

The coming of ice

The position of ice and limits of the land in the British Isles around 20 000 years ago.

World climate has cooled gradually over the last 60 million years, culminating in a rapid cooling about 2 million years ago. This heralded the start of the Quaternary Period and the beginning of the 'Ice Age', a time of major cycles of climate change with fluctuations between cold glacial and warm interglacial periods. We are still in the Quaternary and are currently experiencing an interglacial that began about 10 000 years ago. The Quaternary Period, with its constantly changing climates and the immense erosive power of its glaciers and meltwaters, has had a huge influence on the shape of the landscape around us. Over thousands or even hundreds of years ice and water changed the landscape dramatically. New valleys were gouged out of solid rock by ice and meltwater, drainage patterns were altered and vast quantities of rock debris were dumped as the ice advanced and then melted. Glaciers advanced across the British Isles several times during the Quaternary, each time reshaping the landscape and obliterating much of the evidence of earlier glaciers.

53 Snaefell, viewed from the southeast - a landscape shaped by ice sheets and smoothed by the deposition of rock debris.

The Isle of Man lay directly in the line of ice sheets advancing south from the Scottish Highlands and was probably overrun by ice on several occasions. Our knowledge of glacial activity on the Island is restricted to the last widespread ice advance. Around 30 000 years ago, glaciers advanced out of the mountains of Scotland and the Lake District, covering most of northern Britain and extending into the Irish Sea. For thousands of years the Isle of Man lay buried under a thick blanket of ice which reached its maximum thickness (up to 1000 metres) and extent between 28 000 and 20 000 years ago. These huge ice sheets eroded the landscape, grinding down the land surface and carrying with them vast amounts of sediment. When the ice finally started to melt about 17 000 years ago, material carried by the glaciers was dumped as a thick mantle of clay and rock debris (glacial till), lake muds and outwash sand and gravel. These sediments draped and smoothed the landscape.

54 BACKGROUND: The Jökulsárlón proglacial lake in Iceland.

55 South Barrule is an ice-smoothed hill blanketed with glacial till and a younger covering of peat.

Ice moulds the landscape

56 View of the northern plain with Ramsey in the middle distance and the Bride Hills and Point of Ayre beyond.

*T*he northern plain of the Isle of Man consists entirely of glacial material, much of it carried by glaciers from the west of Scotland or the northern Irish Sea floor. The landscape is dominated by the Bride Moraine which rises to 100 metres above sea level and forms the rolling Bride Hills. The moraine was formed when an ice sheet readvanced southwards over earlier glacial deposits, pushing them like a snow plough. The force of the ice produced spectacular contortions such as folds and thrusts that can be seen today at Shellag Point. There are numerous moraine ridges across the northern plain that reflect former ice limits, of which the Bride Moraine is the best example. The Orrisdale Hills and the Jurby Ridge were also formed at the margins of ice sheets.

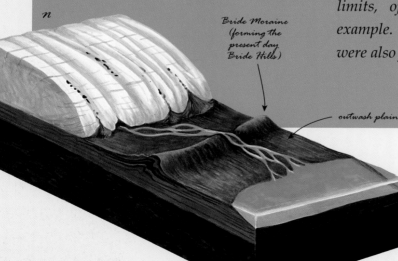

n

Bride Moraine (forming the present day Bride Hills)

outwash plain

S

Formation of the Bride Moraine by readvance and subsequent retreat of a glacier. The lake into which meltwater drained stretched from the east to west coasts of the Isle of Man.

Meltwater from the ice margin drained southwards on to an outwash plain south of the Bride Hills. The channels it created are now preserved as a series of dry valleys. At Jurby the ice sheet plunged into a large lake (known as a proglacial lake) that extended from the east to west coasts and was bounded to the south by the escarpment of the Manx Uplands. The meltwater from this part of the ice drained directly into the lake. Mud from this lake can be seen on the west coast between Killane River and The Cronk, where it contains dropstones deposited by melting icebergs.

57 The Jökulsárlón proglacial lake in Iceland, showing how the area between Killane and Ramsey would have looked about 20 000 years ago.

58 Solifluction terraces in the Rhenass Valley.

Most of the glacial deposits on the Manx Uplands are made of rock debris that was eroded from local rocks such as the granites and the Manx Group. Granite boulders that were plucked from their bedrock source and transported by the ice can be seen on the slopes of South Barrule. Such boulders are known as erratics. Most of the upland glacial deposits are not preserved in situ. After the ice retreated, constant freezing and thawing caused the glacial material to slump and creep downslope towards the valley floors. This process, known as solifluction, produced lobe-shaped landforms which can be seen today. Rivers have since cut into these lobes, producing terraces on valley sides.

Arctic plants and the Irish Elk

*A*round 14 500 years ago, the arctic conditions that had gripped the Isle of Man for so long gave way to a milder, wetter climate. The ice sheet retreated, leaving a scarred and scoured landscape of bare rock and piles of clay, sand and boulders. At this time the Isle of Man was connected by land links to Ireland and Britain. We know from ancient pollen preserved in peat that plants began to colonise the bare land soon after the ice melted. Early colonisers were arctic herbs and dwarf shrubs, and included grasses, mosses, mugwort, saxifrages, crowberry, heathers, juniper, dwarf birch and dwarf willows.

59 Dwarf birch and willow growing today in Iceland.

60 Mountain Avens (*Dryas octopetala*) growing in Iceland. Following ice retreat this plant was one of the arctic plants to colonise the Isle of Man.

The huge quantities of water released by melting ice caused the sea level to rise. As a result the land link between the Isle of Man and Ireland became submerged around 12 000 years ago and the link with Britain was severed about 10 000 years ago.

Pingos (ice-cored hillocks formed in permafrost conditions) left depressions which became filled with lake muds and peat. These deposits preserve fine skeletons of the extinct Irish Elk which in fact was not an elk at all - its closest living relative is the fallow deer. These mighty beasts stood up to 2.1 metres at the shoulder and had an antler span of up to 3.6 metres, dwarfing their modern cousins. These giant deer roamed across Europe and Central Asia for 400 000 years and were thought to have died out over 10 000 years ago. However, a skeleton from Ballaugh has been dated at about 9000 years old, thus making the Isle of Man the home of the youngest reported Irish Elk skeleton in the world, perhaps one of the last of its line.

61 The Irish Elk excavated at Close y Garey in 1887 and displayed in the Manx Museum in Douglas. This skeleton has been dated at about 11 500 years old.

An Irish Elk shown in relation to its closest living relative, the fallow deer.

About 10 000 years ago these giant deer were using the pingo lakes on the Isle of Man as water sources and many died in the boggy lakeside thickets, perhaps ill or injured or starving in winter conditions. Their bones were buried and preserved in the peat, along with the pollen of the plants they fed on. Although it is not known for certain why these animals became extinct, it is thought that the vast amounts of minerals the stags needed to consume in order to grow their huge antlers every year, perhaps coupled with a period of colder climate and poorer vegetation, led to their demise.

37

The Curraghs, the Ayres and the first people

About 11 000 years ago the climate warmed and the arctic scrub and grassland gradually gave way to luxuriant woodland, part of the great wildwood which once covered all but the highest mountain slopes of the British Isles. Birch and willow were established early, followed by pine and hazel, and later by oak, elm and alder. This episode of time, which extends to the present-day, is known as the Holocene and is the most recent division of the Quaternary Period. The Holocene also saw the arrival of the first people on the Isle of Man about 8000 years ago, and from this time onwards human activity was to cause fundamental changes in the landscape of the Island.

62 ABOVE LEFT: Wetland and scrub at the Curraghs.
63 LEFT: The development of peat and decline in tree cover led to heather covered moorland.

The proglacial lake, which lay on the Island's northern plain at the time of the last glaciation, gradually became infilled with peat. This produced a fertile swampy area, patches of which remain today at the Ballaugh Curraghs. This beautiful wetland area is composed of willow and Bog Myrtle scrub, *Sphagnum* bog, ponds and flower-rich meadows. The thick layers of peat were once dug for fuel and have yielded trunks of oak (known as darraghs - the Manx term for bog oak) and Scots Pine as well as Neolithic implements. Today, the area is famous for its rich wetland plant, insect and bird life.

Within the past 5000 years peat-forming *Sphagnum* moss has formed a blanket on the Manx Uplands, creating a wild landscape which appears untouched by human activity. However, many of the peats show a dark charcoal-rich layer near their bases, suggesting that the peat probably formed following the clearing and burning of native woodland from Neolithic times onwards.

At the northern tip of the Isle of Man lies the Ayres, a series of gravel raised beach ridges in front of an ancient cliff-line. The cliff shows that about 9000 years ago the sea level was higher than it is now. The gravel ridges of the Ayres have formed over the past 7000 years and are still accumulating material which is being eroded off the crumbling sea cliffs to the south and transported up the coast by the sea.

The shingle, heathland and marram grass dunes of the Ayres provide important habitats for a wide variety of plants, birds and insects. Flowering plants include the Isle of Man Cabbage, the delicate pink Burnet Rose and several types of orchid. Grey seals can be seen offshore and the area supports breeding colonies of sea birds.

64 LEFT: A Bee Orchid.

The Ayres and other beaches in the north of the Isle of Man, have been used for millennia as a source of boulders, stones, sand and gravel. In Mesolithic, Neolithic and Bronze Age times people collected flint pebbles brought here from Northern Ireland by ice sheets, and made them into implements. Sea-rounded boulders have been used as building stones, and old houses made of shore stones can be seen in Jurby and Bride. Sand and gravel workings continue today near the Point of Ayre and Jurby.

65 FAR LEFT: The Ayres.
66 LEFT: The Isle of Man Cabbage which is common on the northern shores.

The evolving landscape

*A*ltough the Isle of Man has been millions of years in the making, the Island as we would recognise it only came into being about 10 000 years ago with the final disappearance of its land link with Britain. For many centuries the Island's landscape was shaped only by the action of the sea, rivers and weather. The soft cliffs on the northern coasts were eroded, and over time the Island changed shape. Rivers cut down into the bedrock and glacial deposits of the uplands forming valleys and steep sided glens.

68 BOTTOM LEFT: Heather moorland.
69 BOTTOM RIGHT: Mine buildings above Foxdale at 'Snuff the Wind'.

67 Waterfall at Dhoon.

Then, about 8000 years ago, the first settlers arrived and so began a new stage in the evolution of the landscape. Mesolithic and Neolithic impacts on the landscape were most extensive in the lowlands, producing a rich archaeological heritage, but the major landscape changes caused by woodland clearance occurred later, during the Bronze Age. The moorlands of the Manx Uplands that appear a natural landscape owe much of their character to deforestation by Bronze Age and Iron Age people. Through the centuries people have altered the landscape with their agriculture, buildings, graves and mines. Their lives have been shaped by the natural features of the landscape in which they lived, and they in turn have used and changed the appearance of the Island.

Coastal erosion, mainly in the north of the Island, is changing the landscape of the Isle of Man on the scale of a human lifetime. Between The Cronk and Jurby Head the coastline is retreating at a rate of 100 metres per century. The erosion damage is sporadic rather than continuous. For example, in December 1946, a single storm removed a strip of land 2 metres wide and over 3 kilometres long. Records going back 250 years also describe churches and cottages disappearing into the sea. However, as the sea erodes in one place, so it adds to the beaches elsewhere. On the Ayres and along the south side of the Point of Ayre material is being added to the coast at the rate of about 20 to 30 metres per century. The Island's rocky coasts are also changing, although at a slower rate. At The Chasms, great blocks of Manx Group sandstone are breaking along joint planes and gradually slipping into the sea.

70 The eroding cliffs at Ballaugh.

The landscape we see today is a result of the nature of the bedrock, the processes of ice, rivers, weather and sea, and the activities of people through the ages. And it is still evolving.

71 The Chasms.

72 Aerial view with Cregneash village in the foreground, showing the effect of settlements and farming on the landscape.

73 Eroding solifluction deposits in Druidale.

Geologists of the past

*T*he study of the geology and landscape of the Isle of Man spans some 280 years, from the account written in 1722 by Thomas Wilson, Lord Bishop of Sodor and Man, to the most recent geological map and report published by the British Geological Survey in collaboration with the Isle of Man Government in 2001. The intervening years have witnessed the development of many ideas and theories about the geology of the Island and the origins of its rocks, deposits and landscape.

Amongst all the geologists who have worked on the Isle of Man, it is George Lamplugh, an officer of the Geological Survey of England and Wales, who stands out as having made the greatest contribution to our knowledge of the geology of the Island. He was seconded to the Isle of Man Government and spent five years, from 1892 to 1897, producing a geological map of the Island and writing copious notes and observations. Beautifully hand painted copies of his field maps, at the scale of six inches to one mile, are held in the Manx Museum in Douglas. His map of the Isle of Man at one inch to one mile was published in 1898, followed in 1903 by his memoir on the geology of the Island. It is an impressive piece of work. Although many of his interpretations have since been revised, Lamplugh's detailed observations are an invaluable starting point for any study of Manx rocks and his work remains as the most comprehensive account of the Island's geology.

Conserving the Isle of Man's geological heritage

*T*he unique geological sites and landscape features of the Isle of Man are an important and irreplaceable part of the Island's heritage. The rocks and natural features which form the landscape have shaped the character of the Isle of Man - from its soils, plants and wildlife to the lives of the Manx people. To ensure that these sites are preserved for future generations to study and enjoy, Manx National Heritage is leading a group which is in the process of identifying a range of sites to be designated as Regionally Important Geological and Geomorphological Sites (RIGS). The sites are selected on the basis of their educational, scientific or aesthetic value. Many such sites have already been designated by local RIGS working groups in England, Scotland and Wales. The Isle of Man RIGS group will help to manage and conserve the sites through cooperation with landowners and local authorities, and will be involved in raising awareness of our earth science heritage. For further information on RIGS in the Isle of Man please contact Manx National Heritage at the Manx Museum, Douglas.

Acritarch A microfossil of an apparently unicellular organism, made of organic material and of uncertain biological affinity.

Alluvial fan A fan-shaped accumulation of *sediments* that forms at the point where a river passes from a mountainous area to an open plain.

Ammonoids A group of extinct free swimming creatures with coiled shells that first appeared in Devonian times and died out in the Cretaceous.

Amphiboles A group of rock-forming minerals, including the dark green mineral hornblende.

Amygdale A small gas cavity (*vesicle*) in *lava*, which has become infilled with later formed minerals such as *calcite* or *quartz*.

Basalt A dark, fine-grained *igneous extrusive* rock formed when *lava* cools. It consists mainly of the minerals plagioclase (a variety of *feldspar*) and *pyroxene*.

Bed A layer of *sediment* or *sedimentary rock*.

Bronze Age Approximately 4000 to 2600 years ago (2000 BC to 600 BC).

Calcite (calcium carbonate) A rock-forming mineral made of calcium, carbon and oxygen ($CaCO_3$); the main component of *limestone* and *marble*.

Calcrete A hard crust of *calcium carbonate* formed within soil or *sediments* by evaporation of fluids; generally formed in arid and semi-arid environments.

Cleavage plane A plane along which a rock tends to split. Cleavage planes are usually spaced so that a rock (e.g. slate) breaks into parallel-sided slices. Cleavage is formed during deformation or *metamorphism* of the rock (e.g. during tectonic events such as continental collision).

Conglomerate A sedimentary rock formed from the rounded fragments (pebble-sized or larger) of older rocks.

Diorite A speckled black or dark green and white, coarse-grained, igneous intrusive rock, composed mainly of the white mineral plagioclase (a variety of feldspar), and the dark minerals hornblende (a variety of amphibole) and pyroxene.

Dolerite A dark *igneous intrusive* rock, composed of the minerals plagioclase (a variety of *feldspar*) and *pyroxene*. It has the same chemical composition as *basalt* but is coarser grained.

Dropstone A stone that is released from a melting iceberg.

Dyke A sheet-like body of intrusive *igneous* rock which has intruded an earlier formed rock sequence.

Erosion The process by which rock and landscapes are worn away by water, wind or ice.

Erratic A boulder transported by a *glacier* and deposited some distance from the area of bedrock from which it was plucked by the ice.

Fault A fracture in the Earth's crust along which there has been movement.

Feldspars An important group of rock-forming minerals, commonly white or pink.

Foraminifera Microscopic, unicellular marine animals that build chambered skeletons, commonly of *calcium carbonate*. They have inhabited the world's oceans from the Cambrian to the present and live in all levels of the water column.

Freestone A term applied to a building stone that can be cut and worked with equal ease in any direction without splitting.

Gabbro A dark coarse-grained *igneous intrusive* rock, composed of the minerals plagioclase (a variety of *feldspar*) and *pyroxene*. It has the same chemical composition as *basalt* and *dolerite* but is coarser grained.

Gangue The unwanted minerals and rock that are usually found together with economic *ore* minerals. Gangue material is separated from the ore minerals during processing.

Glacier A large mass of ice which flows slowly downhill or outwards under the stress of its own weight.

Glacial till A deposit left by a *glacier* or ice sheet. Till is usually a mixed *sediment* and can include clay, silt, sand, gravel and boulders.

Granite A white, grey or pink, coarse grained *igneous intrusive* rock, composed mainly of the minerals *quartz*, *feldspar* and *mica*.

Graptolite A colony of simple planktonic animals that inhabited the oceans, particularly during the Ordovician and Silurian periods. Graptolites built a range of skeletal structures which are commonly preserved as fossils in dark *mudstone*.

Hematite An important *ore* mineral of iron (Fe_2O_3).

Iapetus Ocean The ocean that existed between the two large continents of Laurentia in the north (comprising present-day North America, Greenland and Scotland) and Gondwana (present-day western Europe, Africa, Australia, Antarctica, South America) around 500 million years ago. A microcontinent, known as Avalonia, lay near the northen margin of Gondwana and included present-day England, Wales and the Isle of Man.

Ice age A term used for any glacial episode, or, more specifically, for the latest glacial period, which ended about 10 000 years ago.

Igneous rock Rock formed when molten rock (*magma*) cools and solidifies. Igneous rocks include extrusive rocks erupted in volcanoes at the Earth's surface (e.g. *basalt*) and intrusive rocks that cool beneath the Earth's surface (e.g. *granite*, *dolerite*, *diorite*).

Iron Age Approximately 2600 to 1800 years ago (600 BC to AD 200).

Joint plane A surface of fracture in a rock. Unlike *faults*, joints do not displace the rock.

Lava A general term for molten rock that is erupted at the Earth's surface and also for the rock that it forms when it cools and solidifies. Pillow lava is erupted underwater, forming bulbous 'pillow' shapes when it comes into contact with water.

Lamprophyre A type of dark coloured *intrusive igneous* rock that contains larger crystals of biotite (a variety of *mica*), hornblende (a variety of *amphibole*) and *pyroxene* in a finer grained mass that also contains *feldspars*.

Limestone A *sedimentary rock* consisting mainly of *calcium carbonate*; commonly formed from the accumulated remains of shelled organisms.

Magma Molten rock from the Earth's interior, which cools and solidifies to form *igneous rocks*. Magma can solidify within the Earth, where it forms igneous intrusions, or at the Earth's surface where it is erupted as lava and cools to form igneous extrusive rocks.

Marble A limestone that has been recrystallised by heat and pressure (i.e. *metamorphism*).

Mesolithic The Middle Stone Age; about 9000 to 5500 years ago (7000 BC to 3500 BC).

Metamorphism The process by which rocks within the Earth's crust are changed by heat and pressure.

Micas A group of minerals that form flat, translucent plates. Mica is silvery white when rich in aluminium (muscovite) and dark when rich in iron (biotite).

Mid-ocean ridge A ridge along an ocean floor, where two plates are pulling apart in a process known as sea floor spreading. As the plates separate, molten rock (*magma*) from the interior of the Earth rises up along the ridge. The magma cools, creating new sea floor.

Mineralisation The process by which minerals are introduced into a rock.

Mineral vein Sheet-like mass of minerals filling fissures or fractures in rock. The minerals crystallise from hot fluids circulating within the Earth's crust.

Moraine A mound or ridge made of material that has been transported and deposited by a *glacier* or ice sheet.

Mudstone A general term for a fine-grained *sedimentary rock* composed of a mixture of clay and silt sized particles.

Neolithic The New Stone Age; about 5500 to 4000 years ago (3500 BC to 2000 BC).

Ore The material (usually a mix of minerals and rock) from which a mineral of economic value is extracted.

Outwash sediments Sand and gravel washed out from a *glacier* by meltwater and deposited in front of the ice.

Permafrost Soil or subsoil which remains frozen all year round.

Pingo An ice-cored hillock formed under *permafrost* conditions. Melting of the ice core produces a rimmed crater. Pingo is an Inuit word meaning 'conical hill'.

Plate tectonics The theory in which it is recognised that the Earth's surface is fragmented into tectonic plates which move across the surface of the planet. The boundaries of these plates interact with each other at plate margins, which are often the site of seismic and tectonic activity (manifested at the Earth's surface as earthquakes and volcanoes).

Proglacial lake A lake formed just beyond the snout of a *glacier*, generally in direct contact with the ice.

Pyroxenes A group of rock-forming minerals; includes the mineral augite, which is common in igneous rocks such as basalt and dolerite.

Quartz A common rock-forming mineral made of silica and oxygen (SiO_2).

Sandstone A *sedimentary rock* formed from hardened layers of sand.

Sediments Loose materials such as sand, silt and clay, that forms as the result of the weathering and *erosion* of rocks. Sediments are carried by water, ice or wind and settle into layers that may eventually harden to become *sedimentary rocks*.

Sedimentary rock A rock type that commonly forms by the hardening of sediments (e.g. *sandstone, siltstone, mudstone*) or from the remains of the hard parts of organisms (e.g. *limestone*). Rocks formed by the evaporation of saline solutions (e.g. rock salt, gypsum) are also termed sedimentary rocks.

Siltstone A fine-grained *sedimentary rock* composed of particles of silt; the material is finer grained than sand and coarser than clay.

Slate A hard, fine-grained rock that splits along cleavage planes; formed by the *metamorphism* of fine-grained *sedimentary rock*.

Solifluction The slow downhill flow of waterlogged soil and scree as a result of alternate freezing and thawing.

Subduction zone A region where plates collide and one plate descends beneath another in a process known as subduction.

Tuff A rock formed from volcanic ash.

Turbidity current An underwater avalanche of mud and sand that flows down a slope and settles to form a *sediment* known as a turbidite deposit.

Unconformity A surface which represents a gap in the geological record; usually formed by a period of *erosion* or a time when no sediments were deposited. Younger rocks therefore lie directly on top of rocks that may be deformed, metamorphosed and many millions of years older.

Vesicle A small cavity in *lava*, formed when gas bubbles became trapped during cooling and solidification (see also *amygdale*).

Acknowledgements

Author and Illustrator: Elizabeth Pickett - geologist at BGS, Edinburgh
Designer: Joyce Barclay - BGS, Edinburgh
Editor: Audrey Jackson - BGS, Keyworth

This book has been produced by the British Geological Survey (BGS) with extensive collaboration from Manx National Heritage (MNH). It is part of a programme of research into the geology of the Isle of Man region, sponsored by TotalFinaElf Exploration UK PLC, in partnership with Enterprise Oil plc and Amerada Hess Limited (the TotalFinaElf/IoM Group). As part of this programme the BGS has also produced a detailed report on the geology of the Isle of Man and its offshore area, and a 1: 50 000 scale solid and drift map of the Island. The Isle of Man's Department of Trade and Industry generously sponsored the printing of this book.

The author and designer would like to thank many people and organisations for providing information and constructive comment, and for permission to use many of the photographs. (Acknowledgement for individual images is provided opposite.) We thank BGS colleagues: Howard Johnson, Rob Barnes, Brian Young, Andrew McMillan, Neil Jones, Nick Riley, Nick Golledge, Jon Merritt, Sue Loughlin, Derek Ball, Elaine Johnston and Stewart Molyneux. We thank Tom Bain, photographer at BGS, Edinburgh, for his expert contribution and Audrey Jackson for editing the book. We are particularly grateful to Manx National Heritage for allowing us to use many of their images and for their help and advice. We especially thank Stephen Harrison, Andrew Foxon, Carola Rush, Kate Hawkins and Roger Sims. We are also grateful for advice from TotalFinaElf Exploration UK staff in Aberdeen, Richard Chiverrell and Geoff Thomas (University of Liverpool), Mark Cooper (Geological Survey of Northern Ireland), Greg Power (University of Portsmouth), David Burnett and David Quirk. Mark Cooper is also thanked for loaning us the ammonoid on the frontispiece. Early drafts were improved by comments from Colin MacDonald, Catherine Pickett, George Pickett and Rachel Flecker.

© NERC & Treasury, Isle of Man 2001.

Acknowledgement of British Geological Survey (NERC) and external copyright photographs. Numbers refer to numbered images in book. Where images are not numbered (e.g. cover, page backdrops), a page number and description is given.

Hand-painted illustrations are by Elizabeth Pickett and design by Joyce Barclay. Unless otherwise stated the NERC photographs (registered numbers provided in brackets where available) were taken by Tom Bain.

© NERC: Cover centre image (P018646), Frontispiece (P104238), Introduction (P018683), 1 (Stewart Molyneux), 2 (P018600), 3 (P018664), 5 (P018716), 11 (P018761), 13 (P018572), 15 (P018566), p12/13 backdrop (P018758), 18 (P018743), 24 (Neil Jones), 25 (Nick Riley), 26 (Neil Jones), 27 (P018796), p21 backdrop (P018796), 32 (Neil Jones), 34 (Neil Jones), 36 (P018651), 39 (P018745), 41 (Nick Riley), 42 (Neil Jones), 43 (Neil Jones), 51 (P018724), 54 (Jon Merritt), 57 (Jon Merritt), 59 (Jon Merritt), 60 (Jon Merritt), 61 (P018808), 63 (P018627), p42 (LSA364.087), p43 backdrop (P018619), p43 inset (P018619), p46/47 backdrop (P018694), Back cover (P018628).

Courtesy of Manx National Heritage: Cover far right image, 4, 6, 7, 8, 9, 14, 19, 20, 22, 29, 30, 31, 35, 37, 44, 45, 46, 47, 48, 49, 50, 52, 55, 62, 64, 65, 66, 67, 68, 69, 70, 71, 72.

G. Power, University of Portsmouth: 16, 17, 23.

Thin section provided by Stephen Crowley, Dept. of Earth Sciences, Univ. of Liverpool: 28.

D. Burnett: 10, 21, 38.

M. Cooper: Cover far left image, 12, 33, 53.

Photographs taken by Dr R. C. Chiverrell (University of Liverpool): 56, 58, 73.

Photograph by C. Heliker, United States Department of the Interior, United States Geological Survey (wwwhvo.wr.usgs.gov/gallery/, accessed 27/8/2001): 40.

Information sources and further reading

The author would like to acknowledge the archives and galleries of the Manx Museum, Douglas, and the Manx National Heritage website (www.gov.im/mnh). The following publications were invaluable information sources for this book and also provide further reading:

General

The Isle of Man: celebrating a sense of place. 1990. V. Robinson and D. McCarroll (editors). Liverpool University Press.

Introduction to geology of the Isle of Man

Manx Mines, Rocks and Minerals. 1994. Resource Pack. Manx National Heritage, Douglas.

The Isle of Man. 1993. Trevor Ford. Geologists' Association Guide Number 46.

The Geology of the Isle of Man. 2001. Trevor Ford, David Burnett and David Quirk. Geologists' Association Guide Number 46.

Irish Elk and fossils

Survival of the Irish Elk into the Holocene. 2000. S. Gonzalez, A. C. Kitchener and A. M. Lister. *Nature*, Vol. 405, pages 753-754.

There's a ratfish in our cellar! 1997. P. E. Ahlberg and M. I. Coates. *Geology Today*, Jan-Feb, pages 20-23.

Detailed geological studies and map

In sight of the suture: the Palaeozoic geology of the Isle of Man in its Iapetus Ocean context. 1999. N. H. Woodcock, D. G. Quirk, W. R. Fitches and R. P. Barnes (editors). Geological Society of London Special Publication Number 160.

Geology of the Isle of Man and its offshore area. 2001. R. A. Chadwick and 16 others. British Geological Survey Research Report, RR/01/06.

Isle of Man, solid and drift geology. 1: 50 000 map series. 2001. British Geological Survey, Nottingham.

The geological timescale on page 4 follows that of F. Gradstein and J. Ogg. 1996. *Episodes*, Vol. 19, pages 3-5.

Archaeology, history and heritage

100 Years of Heritage. The Work of the Manx Museum and the National Trust. 1986. S. Harrison (editor). Manx National Heritage, Douglas.

The Art of the Manx Crosses. 1996. A. M. Cubbon. Manx National Heritage, Douglas.

The Ancient and Historic Monuments of the Isle of Man. 1994. Manx National Heritage, Douglas.

Prehistoric Sites in the Isle of Man. 1995. Manx National Heritage, Douglas.

Location map of the Isle of Man, showing the main roads and some of the places mentioned in the text